SUNDIALS

Angel sundial, Chartres Cathedral, France

SUNDIALS

BY ROY K. MARSHALL

former director, Morehead and Fels Planetariums

ILLUSTRATED BY JERRY CAILOR

THE MACMILLAN COMPANY • NEW YORK
COLLIER-MACMILLAN LTD., LONDON

First Printing

The Macmillan Company, New York
Collier–Macmillan Canada, Ltd., Galt, Ontario
Divisions of the Crowell-Collier Publishing Company

Library of Congress catalogue card number: 63-9340

DESIGNED BY STEFAN SALTER

Preface

While lecturing at the Adler Planetarium over a period of years and, more recently, while acting as Consultant to the Chicago Planetarium Society, I had the opportunity to examine the more than a hundred sundials in the fine collection of antique astronomical instruments assembled by the antiquarian, the late Anton Mensing of the Netherlands, and purchased by Max Adler in 1929 for the Adler Planetarium and Astronomical Museum.

Today our lives are in large measure controlled by exact time as we catch trains and planes, tune in our favorite radio or television programs, or play football or basketball. Schools, businesses, and theatrical performances are operated on precise schedules. We have all become somewhat enslaved by time, and the sundial reminds us that regulation of time has been essential for centuries. Today, this instrument is considered by many to be no more than an interesting ornament, yet it was a most important device through at least thirty-five centuries of recorded history.

As long as the earth continues to rotate on its axis and revolve around the sun, a correctly made and set sundial will tell accurately the kind of time for which it is intended. Yet, too often, a passer-by will pause before a sundial, consult his watch and move away, sadly shaking his head at the thought that anyone could ever have depended on a sundial for correct time.

The fact that the sundial and correctly running watch almost never agree is no reflection on either piece of apparatus. Sundial time is, in the traditional words of the farmer and others, "God's time," as told in the sky; the *standard time* indicated by our clocks and watches is a clever modern invention developed by man for his own convenience. But sundial time can be converted into standard time. If the passer-by mentioned above knows the correction to the sundial for that day, perhaps as engraved on the dial itself, he can apply it and get the correct standard time from the dial.

The proper sundial must be designed and correctly set for the place where it is to be used. It will not give correct time at a different location unless it is of a particular design and is properly readjusted. In Chapter 10, instructions are given on how to construct a type of sundial that is universal—that is to say, it can be set up anywhere from the North Pole to the South Pole. While this book is not designed primarily as a "hobby kit," I hope that many will undertake to construct and use this sundial. In the home it can serve as a conversation piece, and constructing it is a source of instruction in the motions of the earth; its value as a school project needs no elaboration.

Chapters 1 and 2 are truly a brief history of the sundial; for those who wish to pursue the subject, other details can be found in some of the volumes in the list of suggested readings.

Much of this manuscript was written while I was employed as Consultant to the Chicago Planetarium Society, and I wish to express my gratitude to Robert S. Adler, President of the Society and son of Max Adler, donor of the planetarium and astronomical museum to Chicago, and to the Trustees of the Society for permission to publish it. Credit is due also to Robert I. Johnson, director of the Adler Planetarium, for arranging for many of the photographs that illustrate and supplement the text.

Roy K. Marshall

Contents

List of Illustrations

List of Tables

CHAPTER ONE

A Brief History of the Sundial

FROM THE DAWN OF HISTORY TO EGYPT

Whoever made the first sundial, or even where this important achievement took place, we do not know. Even in man's earliest days certain broad divisions of time were forced upon him. The night was a time of terror, spent in whatever cave or other shelter was available, withdrawn from a world populated with beasts in search of prey. Only after daybreak could man emerge from his place of hiding to forage for his own food. But he had to mark the passage of the day so there would be sufficient time for him to find shelter before the coming of night. The sun was man's friend and benefactor, even worshiped as the god that gave light and warmth; the night was his enemy.

Very early in man's career he must have observed how the shadows slanted. To an observer in the northern hemisphere, the shadows were longest and pointed westward in

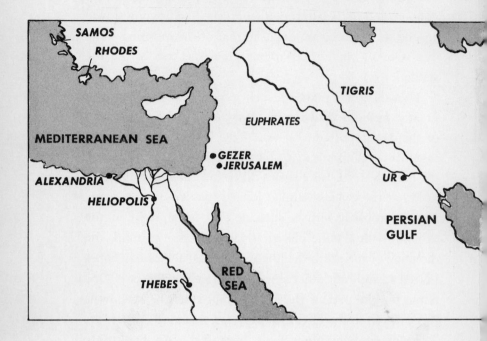

Map of the Fertile Crescent. This area at the eastern end of the Mediterranean was the location of the Sumerian, Assyrian, Babylonian, and Egyptian civilizations.

the morning. They were shortest and pointed northward at noon, and in the afternoon lengthened and swung slowly around to the direction opposite that of the morning shadows. Out of such observations grew the concept of the sundial.

Thousands of years of such experience preceded this great invention. When man considered marking the hours of the day important, he must have been a civilized creature in an organized society, living in communities, planning his life, aware of his responsibilities to those around him.

What the earliest sundial looked like we do not know. It was probably only a stick or post set upright in the ground, with a stone placed at some distance to mark the direction of the post's shadow at noon and additional stones placed to indicate other important times of the day. One name for the part of the sundial that casts the shadow is the *style,* from the Greek word *stylos,* meaning "pillar."

So many beginnings have been lost. We have only secondhand reports from unreliable sources about the origin of the sundial. Herodotus (*c.* 484–425 B.C.), the Greek historian, stated that the sundial originated in, or at least was imported from, Babylonia in Asia—the country in the valley of the Tigris and Euphrates Rivers where so much of our western culture was born. We owe to these people the divisions of 24 hours of day and night (although different from ours), 360 degrees in the circle, 12 months of the year, and 7 days of the week.

Originally, there were always twelve hours of day and

A primitive man and his shadow post.

twelve of night, each of these hours divided into two half-hours. But, everywhere except at the earth's equator, the days are longer than the nights for six months and shorter than the nights for the remaining six months.

It would be enormously complicated to have each hour of daylight one and two-third times as long in June as in December. Yet this would be the fact in the northern United States if there were twelve hours of day and twelve of night all year, because in those states the sun is above the horizon for fifteen of our present hours on June 22 and for only nine hours on December 22. It is somewhat amazing to learn that our twenty-four equal-hour division of the day and night was not strongly urged until the early thirteenth century A.D. by the Arabian astronomer Abul-Hassan, and was not generally accepted until about the fifteenth century.

It is possible that Abraham, the first patriarch and "father" of the Hebrew people, and his family brought with them the learning of the civilization "between the rivers," including the calendar and the sundial. Abraham came from Ur of the Chaldees (a name for Babylonia), as we can read in Genesis 11:31, at a time variously estimated from 2150 B.C. to 1500 B.C. (The latter date has been recently advanced by the scholar Professor Claus Schedl of the University of Graz, in Austria, from his study of errors made in translating Hebrew numbers from various ancient manuscripts.)

References in the Old Testament are usually considered

to be the earliest literary mention of a sundial; in the King James Version we read:

> Behold, I will bring again the shadow of the degrees, which is gone down in the sun dial of Ahaz, ten degrees backward. So the sun returned ten degrees, by which it was gone down.
>
> (ISAIAH 38: 8)

The same, probably apocryphal, event is described elsewhere:

> And Isaiah the prophet cried unto the Lord, and he brought the shadow ten degrees backward, by which it had gone down in the dial of Ahaz.
>
> (II KINGS 20: 11)

There is some confusion in the passage from Isaiah: both the shadow and the sun are said to have gone down; whereas if the sun were going down, the shadow would be going out or up. Another translation, the American Revised Version, gives us a possible clue to the nature of this dial:

> Behold, I will cause the shadow on the steps, which is gone down on the dial of Ahaz with the sun, to return backward ten steps. So the sun returned ten steps on the dial whereon it was gone down.

Ahaz (*c.* 751–*c.* 727 B.C.) reigned in Judah, an ancient kingdom in southern Palestine. We do not know what this Dial of Ahaz was like or whether the instrument was inside or outside the building. The illustration shows an imaginary reconstruction of the device. If the instrument were

Imaginary reconstruction of the Dial of Ahaz.

inside a building, a hole in the roof would have admitted the sunlight, and the position of its shadow on the steps would indicate the time. The steps, however, may have been those of a building in Jerusalem, and the shadow of a corner of another building indicated the time as it moved on them.

The earliest existing sundial is in the Berlin Museum. It is an Egyptian *shadow stick* bearing the name of "the Napoleon of ancient Egypt," Thothmes (also Thutmose or Tuthmosis) III, who ruled from Thebes between about 1504 and 1450 B.C. Only a horizontal bar, inscribed with time marks, remains. From illustrations on temple walls, it is known that the shadow stick originally had an upright T-shaped structure to cast the shadow at one end. In the morning, the bar was turned so the T was facing east and the shadows fell on the bar to the west. At noon, the device was reversed, with the T to the west, the shadows falling on the bar to the east.

The hours counted by this early Egyptian sundial were unequal. Only about five and one-half "hours" could be indicated by marks on the stick; by the reversal at noon, a total of eleven could be timed. But in winter these would be the equivalent of about nine and one-half of our hours, and in summer they would amount to about twelve and one-half. The earliest hour or so in the morning and the latest in the afternoon could not be counted at all because the shadow cast by the stick would stretch to infinite length. In the illustration, the shadow indicates that the

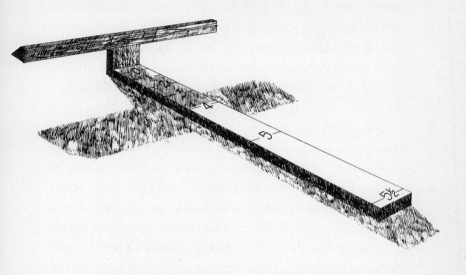

Modern reconstruction of the shadow stick of
Thothmes III.

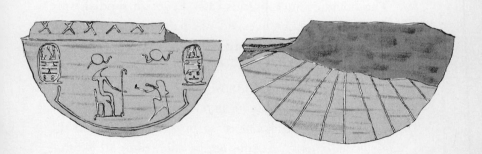

Drawing of the sundial dating from the period of
Merneptah.

time is four hours from noon, and, because the shadow of
the T-shaped *gnomon* falls toward the observer, it must be
morning.

The next oldest sundial that has been found dates from
the period of the Egyptian king Merneptah (also Meneptah
or Merenptah, ruled 1232–1224 B.C.); it was unearthed
at Gezer, in south Palestine, about twenty-five miles northwest of Jerusalem. This area was occupied by Egypt during
that period. A semicircular disk of ivory, it is divided into
twelve sections; at the point where the marks converge is
a hole in which a shadow-casting stick, perhaps a thin rod
of ivory, once stood. We do not know exactly how this
instrument was used because no illustrations of it have been
found, nor any description of how it was held or placed in
position to tell the time. In the imaginary reconstruction
on the reverse side of the disk, at right and left, are *car-
touches* (names enclosed in oval frames) of Merneptah
with other figures between them.

CHAPTER TWO

A Brief History of the Sundial

FROM CLASSICAL GREECE TO THE PRESENT

Various Greek scientists from the sixth century B.C. onward are known to have invented, or at least to have possessed, sundials of various forms. According to the Roman naturalist and author, Pliny the Elder (Caius Plinius Secundus, 23–79 A.D.), the Greek philosopher Anaximenes of Miletus, in Asia Minor, who lived in the middle or the second half of the sixth century B.C., had a sundial of the form called *sciotherion*; unfortunately nothing is known about this instrument.

The invention of the bowl-shaped form of sundial called the *hemispherium* is usually credited to the Chaldean priest-astronomer Berosus who lived in the time of Alexander the Great (356–323 B.C.), king of Macedon. But some authorities believe that the originator of this type of sundial was either the Greek mathematician and astrono-

Cleopatra's Needle in Central Park, New York City.

mer Eudoxus of Cnidus (408–355 B.C.) or the Greek mathematician Apollonius of Perga (250–180 B.C.)— both locations are in Asia Minor.

In 1852, a stone *hemicyclium*, a sundial in the form of a partial bowl, was found at the foot of Cleopatra's Needle in Alexandria; it is now in the British Museum. The photograph shows the second Cleopatra's Needle now located in Central Park, New York City. (These two inscribed red granite obelisks were erected by Thothmes III at Heliopolis, "City of the Sun," at the apex of the Nile delta in

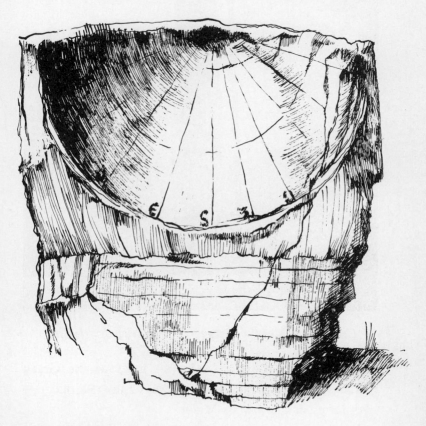

The hemicyclium found at the foot of one of Cleopatra's Needles in 1852.

Egypt in 1455 B.C. The Roman emperor Augustus, 63 B.C.–14 A.D., moved them to Alexandria.)

In the drawing of the hemicyclium (p. 27), the time marks—indicated by Greek letters, which also served as numerals—can be seen. The lettering is evidence that this device dates from the period after Alexander the Great occupied Egypt in 332 B.C. The gnomon, the upright part of the sundial that casts the shadow, is missing, but originally it must have extended horizontally from the top of the back of the cavity.

An unusual sundial is shown in the close-up photograph of a modern hemicyclium located in New York's Central Park. This large bench, dedicated to the memory of Waldo Hutchins (1822–1891), one of the founders of Central Park, is at once a place of rest and a sundial. On the pavement in front of the bench are curved marks indicating where the shadow of the bench falls at 10:00 A.M., noon, and 2:00 P.M. on March 31 and September 23.

The flat dial resembling the most common type of sundial seen today is said by some to have been devised by the Greek astronomer Aristarchus of Samos (310–230 B.C.). We do know that the Greek astronomer and geographer Eratosthenes (276–194 B.C.), the librarian of the great museum at Alexandria, used a vertical gnomon on a horizontal surface to work out astronomical problems, including that of the earth's circumference.

The first sundial in Rome was set up in 293 B.C. by the Roman general Papirius Cursor in the court of the Temple

A monumental sundial in Central Park. The close-up view is of the hemicyclium mounted on the back of the bench.

of Quirinus (an ancient Italic god of war and agriculture), and by the year 200 B.C. the timing devices were fairly common. Many of these Roman sundials were acquired as part of the plunder of other cities throughout the Mediterranean and were placed in new positions with no regard for their points of origin. They could not, therefore, indicate the correct time for Rome. The Romans had little if any understanding of the principles of the construction and operation of sundials, and most of these instruments were merely ornamental curiosities to them. The Roman civilization—so magnificent in literature, art and architecture, law and military tactics—was sadly deficient in pure science and philosophy.

Good sundials could not be constructed until the principles of geometry and trigonometry were understood. This is because the position of the shadow of the gnomon depends upon the shape and orientation of the dial, its location on the earth, and the place of the sun in the sky—a somewhat complicated geometrical problem. Early geometers worked by "rule of thumb" and often did not set down any formal rules for others to follow. About 300 B.C., Euclid (c. 323–c. 285 B.C.), a Greek mathematician then at Alexandria, collected the principles of geometry known in his day and added some of his own; he demonstrated rigid proofs of the earlier geometrical constructions and thereby became the founder of the formal study of this important branch of mathematics.

The foundations of trigonometry are credited to the

great Greek astronomer Hipparchus (160?–125? B.C.) who was born in Bithynia in northwest Asia Minor. His work made possible the constructions of *astrolabes*, the ancient devices for working out problems of time and navigation, and some forms of sundials. But it was more than a thousand years before Albategnius (the Arab mathematician and astronomer Al-Battani, 850–929 A.D.) put trigonometry on a formal basis, and, not until then that *dialling*, as the art of making sundials and other similar instruments is called, became relatively easy and popular—at least among scholars. For about nine centuries after Albategnius, the sundial reigned supreme as the standard timekeeper. *Sand glasses* and *clepsydras*, or water clocks (literally, "water thief"), were used in cloudy weather and at night, but the sundial was the standard against which these devices were checked.

The early water clocks were of two types. In one, a bowl with a small hole in the bottom was set in a larger container of water. When the smaller bowl filled with water and sank, one interval of time had passed, the subdivisions of the interval being indicated by marks inside the bowl. In the other type only one bowl was used. It was filled with water, which trickled out slowly through a hole near the bottom; when the bowl was empty, one time interval had passed. Later, clepsydras were used in both Greece and Rome to time the speeches of politicians. Water from one container slowly flowed into another which contained a float. As the float rose with the water level, it activated a

A water clock.

A South German seventeenth-century hourglass.

single hand that marked the hour on a clock face. The photograph from the Mensing Collection shows a water clock made in London in 1691. In this device, the level of the water in the cylindrical tank fell, and as the float sank it pulled the chain, moving the hand on the clock.

Sand glasses (sometimes familiarly called "hourglasses") were a later invention. These instruments could not be made until glass of good quality became available, because it was essential that the sand trickling from the upper

An eighteenth-century hourglass, with wooden frame.

portion into the lower be visible as well as dry. When all of the sand was in the lower chamber, the instrument was inverted to let the sand run the other way. It is usually thought that the sand glass came into existence in Middle and Northern Europe where the water in a clepsydra would freeze during the winter, whereas sand would continue to flow. The invention is sometimes attributed to the eighth-century monk Luitprand, of Chartres, France.

During the centuries when the sundial was the primary timekeeper, travelers carried portable sundials, some of which could be neatly folded into small packages no larger

Urs Graf's "Young Man Consulting a Pocket Dial."

than a fat "grandfather's watch" of a century ago. The pen drawing by the Swiss artist Urs Graf (*c.* 1485–*c.* 1527) of a "Young Man Consulting a Pocket Dial" shows what is

Two collapsible pocket dials. (LEFT) *An early seven-teenth-century German horizontal dial. The gnomon can be folded flat and the lid then closed. The magnetic compass permits proper alignment of the gnomon.* (RIGHT) *A late sixteenth-century equatorial sundial. The gnomon is the thin spike, which can be folded down into the plane of the ring; then the ring can be placed flat against the compass case.*

probably a collapsible *equatorial* dial (pp. 49–52). The "sunwatch" is another collapsible dial—a portable, *horizontal* one (p. 50) recommended for Boy Scout use. It has three settings for the collapsible gnomon, and a different

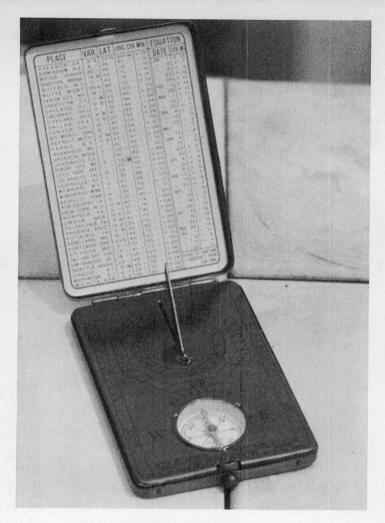

The "Sunwatch."

dial for each setting. The small magnetic compass permits alignment of the instrument. When closed, this modern pocket sundial is only ⅜ by 2 by 3 inches in size.

In the sixteenth century, a literary reference to a sundial

appears in Shakespeare's *As You Like It*. In Act II, scene 7, Jaques, a member of the duke's court, describes his encounter with Touchstone, the jester:

> "Good-morrow, fool," quoth I: "No, sir," quoth he,
> "Call me not fool till heaven hath sent me fortune."
> And then he drew a dial from his poke,
> And, looking on it with lack-lustre eye,
> Says very wisely, "It is ten o'clock:
> Thus may we see," quoth he, "how the world wags.
> 'Tis but an hour ago since it was nine;
> And after one hour more 'twill be eleven;
> And so, from hour to hour, we ripe and ripe,
> And then, from hour to hour, we rot and rot;
> And thereby hangs a tale."

Sundials from very early times have been imprinted with bits of philosophy, some happy, others more profound and somber, concerned with the inexorable march of time or the shortness of man's life on earth.

Some legends found on sundials are these:

> I count none but sunny hours.

> May all your hours be as sunny as those I count.

> Haste, traveler, the sun is sinking now;
> He shall return again, but never thou.

> *Carpe diem* ("seize the moment").

> *Nulla fluit cuius non meminisse juvet*
> ("Let no hour pass which is not a delight to remember").

> *Redibo, tu nunquam* ("I shall return, thou never").

> *Umbra sumus—tamen his aevum componitur umbris*
> ("We are a shadow—yet time is made up of such shadows").

And, finally, one legend that compares the accuracy of the sundial with the very erratic behavior of some of the early public clocks, with their bells striking the hours:

> *Può fallare la campana il ferro*
> *Ma risplende il sole Io non erro.*

which can be translated:

> The iron bell may wrongly tell;
> I err not, if the sun shine well.

CHAPTER THREE

The Sun's Apparent Daily Motion and Shadows

To tell time by reading a sundial, it is necessary to understand the underlying principles by which the instrument functions. The shadows, indicating time as they fall on the dial, are dependent upon the *apparent daily motion* of the sun. The sun rises in the east and sets in the west, and the earth rotates eastward on its axis completely once each twenty-four hours; the stars, the planets, the moon, and the sun all *appear* to roll westward over us: this is apparent daily motion.

For an observer in the northern hemisphere facing south, the sun rises at his left, climbs upward to the right, stands highest in the sky at noon, then declines to the right,

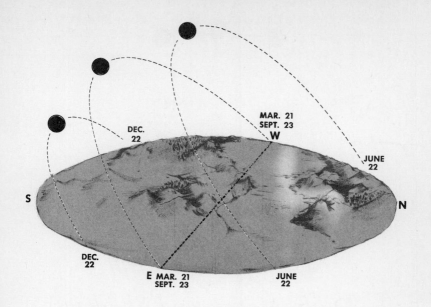

NORTHERN HEMISPHERE

Diurnal path of the sun: Northern Hemisphere.

or westward, during the afternoon. For an observer in the southern hemisphere facing north the sun rises at the right, climbs upward to the left, and then declines to the left. In the drawing, the sun's daily path for June 22, December 22, March 21, and September 23 are shown for an observer: (p. 41) in a mid-northern latitude; (p. 42) at the equator; (p. 43) in a mid-southern latitude.

The closer to the *equator* the observer is located, the steeper is the sun's apparent daily path. In the tropic zone, between *latitudes* 23½ degrees north and 23½ degrees south, the sun stands in the *zenith,* the point directly over-

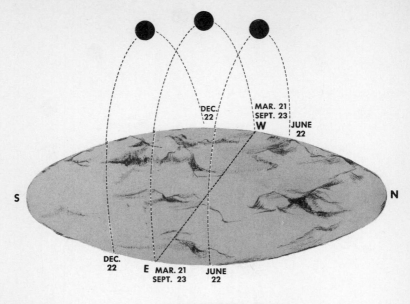

EQUATOR

Diurnal path of the sun: Equator.

head, on certain days of the year. For an observer on the earth's equator, the sun remains above the *horizon* for just twelve hours every day of the year. And, for this observer, the sun rises north of east from March 21 to September 23 and sets north of west; for the remaining six months, it rises south of east and sets south of west.

Traveling farther from the equator, one finds more daylight than night for six months and a longer night than day for the remaining six months. At the North Pole, the sun remains above the horizon from March 21 to September 23, and is below the horizon for the other half of the

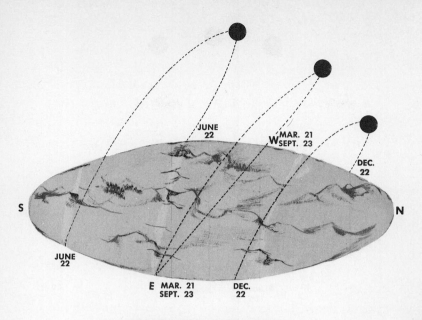

SOUTHERN HEMISPHERE

Diurnal path of the sun: Southern Hemisphere.

year. At the South Pole, the sun is above the horizon from September 23 to March 21 and below it for the remainder of the year.

If the sun is in the east during the morning hours, shadows lie to the west of the objects that cast them. In the afternoon, the shadows lie to the east. In the northern hemisphere, with the sun in the south at noon, shadows lie to the north; and because the sun is then highest in the sky, the shadows are shortest. In the southern hemisphere, with the sun highest in the north at noon, the shadows are to the south and are shortest for the day.

Exactly at the points designated as the poles, there is no east or west. At the North Pole, every direction is south; at the South Pole, every direction is north.

Let us imagine that we are exactly at the North Pole and that there is indeed a real, physical North Pole—a thin rod standing upright so that it points directly toward the zenith, like an extension of the *axis* (the imaginary axle on which the earth rotates). We will further suppose that the sun remains above the horizon and that the sky is clear for at least twenty-four hours.

At every moment the post will cast a shadow in the direction exactly opposite to that of the sun. As the earth rotates, the shadow will appear to swing around the post, but in reality it is the snowy surface beneath the shadow that revolves.

The simple experiment just described illustrates a very important and fundamental fact about time and time-keepers: The earth rotates once in twenty-four hours; the shadow of the post swings completely around the 360 degrees of a circle in twenty-four hours. Therefore, each hour is the equivalent of 15 degrees.

Let us consider again the imaginary post at the North Pole. If we marked twenty-four equally spaced divisions on a circular sheet of cardboard, each line would be exactly 15 degrees away from its neighboring lines. A hole could be cut in the center of the circle and the card slipped over the imaginary rod so that the disk lies flat on the snow. As the earth rotates, and the shadow appears to swing

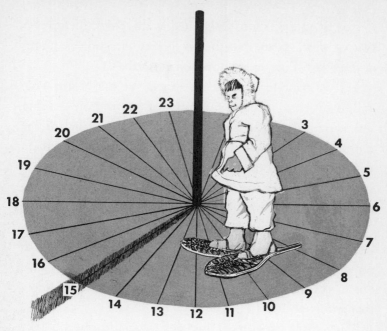

NORTH POLE

A simple gnomon and dial at the North Pole.

clockwise along the face of the card, we can read off the passage of the hours, each 15 degree division representing one hour. This is a sundial, good for that one spot on earth —the North Pole.

If we are at the South Pole and a similar rod pointing to the zenith has been set up with a disk again marked into twenty-four equal divisions, what do we see as the earth turns on its axis? As each hour passes, the shadow of the

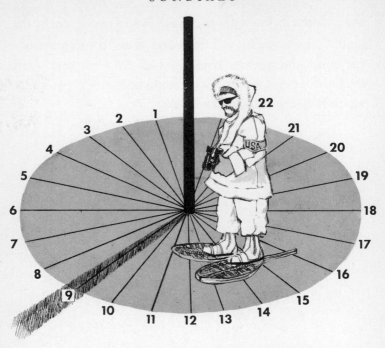

SOUTH POLE

A simple gnomon and dial at the South Pole.

rod moves to the next line on the card, just as before; but now the shadow appears to swing around counterclockwise, because at the South Pole the apparent daily motion of the sun is from right to left—instead of from left to right as at the North Pole. This equipment will give equally accurate readings at both of the poles, but the numbers corresponding to the hours of the day must be arranged in such a way that they increase clockwise for the North Pole and counterclockwise for the South Pole. Consequently, the sundial cannot be moved from one place to another without some adjustments. This is one of the first rules about sundials: They can be used correctly only at the places for which they are designed and set up.

CHAPTER FOUR

The Equatorial Sundial and Other Sundial Types

All sundials consist of two basic components: the dial and the gnomon. They are classified according to the arrangement of these parts.

The dial, on which the shadow falls to indicate time, is named from the medieval Latin word *dialis*, which in turn came from the Latin word *dies* (day); *dialis* means daily. The rod or any edge casting a shadow that falls on the dial is the gnomon, from a Greek word meaning "one who knows." A proper gnomon associated with a proper dial "knows how to" mark the correct time on the dial.

The different sundials get their names from the manner in which the time dial lies on the instrument. If the dial

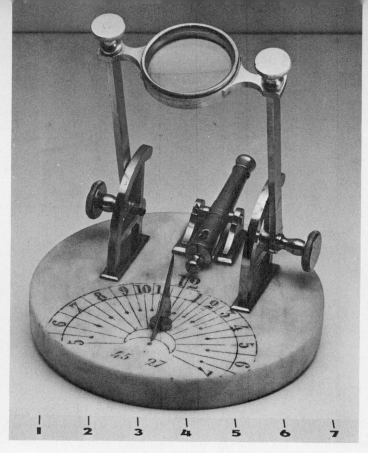

A brass and marble French sundial of the early nine-teenth century. The little cannon of this horizontal dial could be loaded and at noon it would fire. At this time of day, the sun's rays, concentrated by the burning glass, ignited the powder in the hole near the breech of the cannon.

lies parallel to the plane of the equator, the instrument is called the *equatorial* sundial. The most common construction has a dial that is always horizontal, and this is called

A late sixteenth-century portable ring sundial from southern Germany. Instead of the more usual small hole to admit the sunlight to the time scale on the inside of the ring, this dial uses a notch in one edge. To operate the instrument, the user suspended it by a cord and turned it to line up with the direction of the sun at that moment.

the *horizontal* sundial. The dial can also be vertical, in which case the instrument is called a *vertical* sundial. Some portable sundials are ring-shaped, like wide bracelets, hanging by short cords, and these are named *ring* sundials. Other portable sundials, used even in this century by shepherds in the Pyrenees Mountains, between France and

Spain, are shaped like cylinders; these are called *chilindre,* or pillar, sundials because the time marks are arranged on the outside of the cylindrical form.

In order to discuss some additional reference points, let us go again to the North Pole of the earth. The axis of the earth, the imaginary axle on which it turns, extends straight down from our feet, but if we extend the axis outward into space, it passes through the *zenith,* the point exactly overhead. This point in the sky is called the *north celestial pole* because it is exactly above the earth's North Pole. Similarly, the *south celestial pole* is the point in the heavens exactly over the earth's South Pole. And midway between these two celestial poles is an imaginary circle all around the sky, exactly over the earth's equator; this circle is the *celestial equator.* The dial of an equatorial sundial is parallel to the celestial equator as well as to that of the earth.

An equatorial sundial is a universal instrument because it can be used anywhere on earth simply by tilting the whole device. In most modern sundials, the gnomon is parallel to the earth's axis. Therefore, in the equatorial sundial the gnomon is perpendicular to the dial, because the axis of the earth is perpendicular to the equator. In the horizontal sundial, the gnomon is slanted at a particular angle, depending on the place for which the dial is constructed. This means that the time dial must be properly constructed for the place and that the instrument cannot be moved very far north or south without impairing its accuracy.

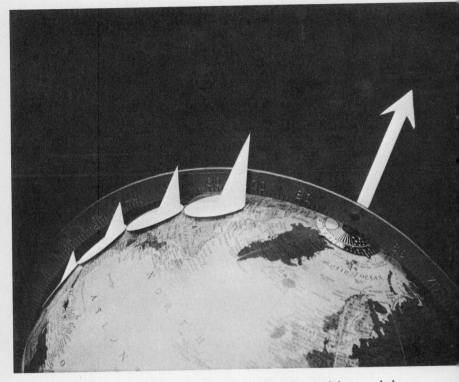

Model horizontal sundials mounted on a library globe.

In the figure, simple model sundials of the common horizontal type have been attached to a library globe at latitudes 15°, 30°, 45°, and 60° north. Note that the south (left-hand) slanted edges of all the gnomons are parallel to each other and to the arrow pointing to the north celestial pole. The slant of each gnomon is equal to the latitude where it is placed.

CHAPTER FIVE

The Angular Equivalent of Time

The location of a place on the earth's surface is expressed in these terms of measurement: *longitude* and *latitude*. Longitude is stated either in *angular* or time measurement. The zero *meridian* of longitude is an imaginary line that runs from the North Pole to the South Pole, passing through the London suburb, Greenwich, England. On a globe of the earth, the point where this meridian crosses the equator is marked by a zero. The figure shows the part of the earth that is centered on the zero meridian. The equator and the zero meridian of longitude have been marked heavily; the arrows indicate the directions for measuring latitude and longitude; the vertical lines are longitude meridians, 15 degrees, or one hour, apart. When the sun appears to stand over the zero meridian, it is noon at Greenwich and at all places on the same meridian.

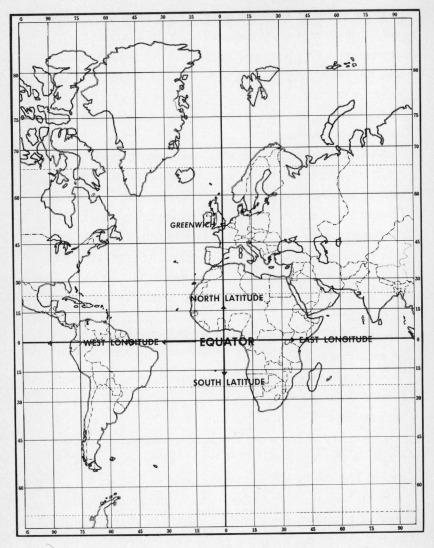

The portion of the earth centered on the zero meridian.

If the meridian for some other place crosses the equator just 15 degrees west of this zero point, its longitude is 15 degrees west. One hour after the sun is over the zero meridian, the earth will have turned eastward through 15 degrees; it is noon along the meridian just 15 degrees west of Greenwich, and one o'clock in the afternoon for the meridian of Greenwich.

New York and Philadelphia have longitudes close to 75 degrees west (every 15 degrees is the equivalent of one hour), and this means that five hours after it is noon at Greenwich, it is noon in Philadelphia and New York, and of course, it is then 5:00 P.M. at Greenwich. The abbreviation P.M. stands for *post meridiem*, the Latin for "after the middle of the day." Similarly, A.M. stands for *ante meridiem*, the Latin for "before the middle of the day." The correct abbreviation for noon is 12:00 M., which means 12 *meridiem*, or "12, the middle of the day." Midnight should be abbreviated as 12:00 P.M.

Every owner of a sundial should know how to convert from angular measure to time and from time to angular measure. In order to read the time properly from a sundial, it is necessary to know the longitude correction, which depends on the longitude of the place where the sundial is set up. This correction will be discussed in Chapter 7.

From here on, the symbols used to designate the divisions of time and angle will be used. There are 360 degrees (360°) in a complete circle. One degree (1°) contains 60 minutes (60′); one minute contains 60 seconds

One corner of the Central Park Quadrant of the United States Geological Survey Map.

*A brass late seventeenth-century French sundial with
silvered face. The magnetic compass and leveling
screws were used to set the instrument.*

($60''$). Day and night combined contain 24 hours (24^h). Each hour has 60 minutes (60^m) and each minute 60 seconds (60^s). Angular measure is usually called *arc*.

Table 1.   Conversion of Time to Arc and Arc to Time

TIME TO ARC	ARC TO TIME
$1^h = 15°$	$1° = 4^m$
$1^m = 15'$	$1' = 4^s$
$1^s = 15''$	$1'' = 1/15^s$

Suppose our longitude is $77°27'45''$. This information could be obtained from a county surveyor or city engineer who establish such measurements, or it could be determined from a large, accurate map, such as those sold through map stores by the United States Geological or Geographical Survey. Let us determine now the time equivalent of this angular measurement.

$$
\begin{array}{ccc}
\text{ARC} & & \text{TIME} \\
77° = 308^m & = & 5^h08^m \\
27' = 108^s & = & 01^m48^s \\
\underline{45'' = 3^s} & = & \underline{03^s} \\
77°27'45'' & = & 5^h09^m51^s
\end{array}
$$

Thus the difference in longitude between us and Greenwich is the difference in time between us: the longitude difference of $77°27'45''$ is equal to a time difference of $5^h09^m51^s$. When it is noon at longitude $77°27'45''$ west, it is 5:09:51 P.M. at Greenwich, England.

CHAPTER SIX

Latitude

Longitude is the location of a place eastward or westward from the meridian of Greenwich; in the same way, latitude locates a place northward or southward from the earth's equator. Latitude is always expressed in degrees, never in time, and never exceeds 90°.

If a place is on the earth's equator, the latitude is 0°. If the location is the North Pole, the latitude is 90° N., or +90°. At the South Pole, the latitude is 90° S., or −90°. Halfway between the equator and the North Pole is the latitude +45°, and so on. This is a simple concept, but a very important one in connection with sundials. One degree of latitude is, on the average, close to sixty-nine miles in length on the earth's surface. Sundials should be correctly set for the latitude of their location; therefore, an instrument cannot be moved any appreciable distance north or south without rendering it incapable of yielding correct time.

Anyone who wishes to purchase and set up a sundial, or to make one, should know his latitude, which again can be found from county surveyor, city engineer, or scaled off from the large-scale maps prepared by the government agencies mentioned earlier. Such maps are fascinating in themselves, showing every street and highway, every railroad track, churches, schools, and many other public buildings—even many residences, public parks, and other points for which very accurate values of longitude and latitude have been determined.

The latitude of the place where a sundial is to be set up relates to the sundial's construction. We might imagine once more that we are at the North Pole, where the gnomon of our sundial stood vertically, pointing to the north celestial pole, exactly in the zenith. If we move just $1°$ away from the North Pole, the north celestial pole will no longer stand in the zenith, but will be $1°$ away from it. Therefore, $1°$ away from the North Pole, our latitude is $+89°$. Also, if the north celestial pole is just $1°$ away from the zenith, its *altitude,* or angular distance above the horizon, is $89°$, because the altitude of the zenith is $90°$.

If we move southward until we are $30°$ from the North Pole (that would be about 2,070 miles from the Pole), our latitude will be $+60°$. The north celestial pole will then appear to be $30°$ away from the zenith, so its altitude will be $60°$. To summarize this: The latitude of a place is

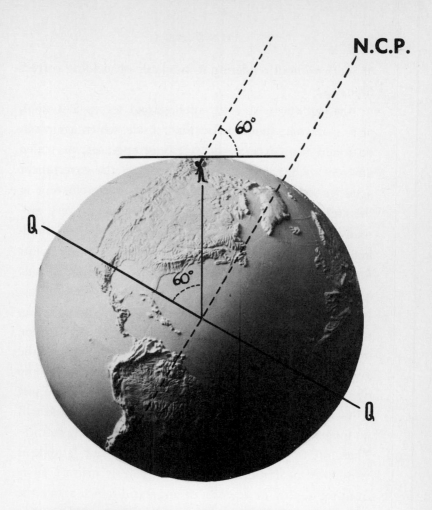

ALTITUDE OF POLE EQUAL TO LATITUDE OF PLACE

The relation between the latitude of a place and the altitude of the celestial pole.

equal to the altitude of the celestial pole as it appears from that place.

It was pointed out earlier that the gnomon of a sundial should slant so that it is parallel to the axis of the earth, which, when extended outward to "touch" the sky, indicates the celestial pole. Therefore, if the gnomon of the sundial is pointed to the celestial pole, it it also parallel to the earth's axis.

The celestial pole is not easy to locate in the sky, but it is not always necessary to find it. Since the altitude of the celestial pole is equal to the latitude of the location, we simply have to tilt the gnomon of the sundial until its edge is slanted upward from the horizontal by an angle equal to our latitude. Once the angle is correct, the gnomon should be lined up pointing exactly north and south. This north-south line could be determined by a surveyor, but it can be found most easily from the sundial itself, as we shall see when the cutout equatorial sundial is being constructed.

CHAPTER SEVEN

Standard Time
and the Longitude Correction

Most people are under the impression that sundials cannot tell correct time. They can. But to obtain the right time for a given place, corrections have to be applied. In the next two chapters these correction factors will be explained.

As we have seen in Chapter 5, only places exactly on the same meridian can have the same time at any given moment. The actual time, the "real time" as indicated by shadows, for any place located even a fraction of a degree away from that meridian would therefore be different; and if time were told by "real" time, considerable confusion would result.

Below are listed several cities in which correctly set

watches and clocks all read the same, yet the "real" times by the sun are all different, because the longitudes are different. When it is exactly noon by the sun in Philadelphia, the "real" time for the localities listed below is:

Table 2. Some Cities and Their "Real" Times

Eastport, Maine	12:32 P.M.
Boston, Massachusetts	12:16 P.M.
New York, New York	12:04 P.M.
Philadelphia, Pennsylvania	12:00 M.
Washington, D. C.	11:52 A.M.
Chapel Hill, North Carolina	11:44 A.M.
Miami, Florida	11:44 A.M.
Cleveland, Ohio	11:37 A.M.
Detroit, Michigan	11:28 A.M.
Cincinnati, Ohio	11:22 A.M.

Of course, many other towns could be cited for each of these times: Buffalo, New York, is very nearly on the same meridian as Chapel Hill, North Carolina; Roanoke, Virginia, Charleston, South Carolina, and Pittsburgh, Pennsylvania, are on the same meridian as Miami, Florida; Augusta, Georgia, and Cleveland, Ohio, are on the same meridian; Tallahassee, Florida, and Atlanta, Georgia, have the same longitude as Cincinnati, Ohio.

The railroads led the way to a standardization of time; their timetables were ridiculously complicated by recognition of all the local times. The idea of standard time was proposed and, in some measure, put into effect at an international conference in Washington, D.C., in 1884, but not

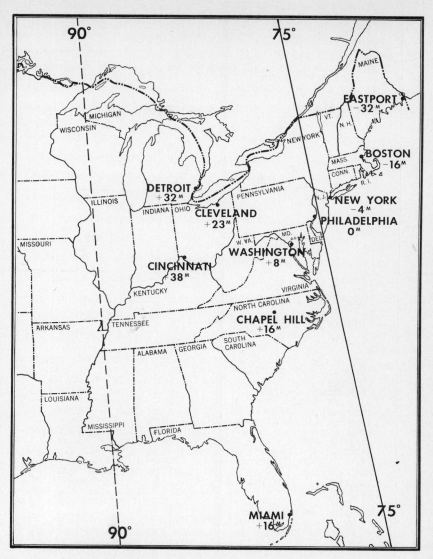

The Eastern United States. Locations listed in the table are shown, with their longitude corrections. The heavy line passing near Philadelphia is the Eastern standard time meridian; the broken line running from Wisconsin through Mississippi is the Central standard time meridian.

until 1918 did the United States officially adopt the scheme and outline the standard time zones.

Broad north-south swaths of the country have agreed to keep the same standard time, the "correct" time for a meridian of longitude roughly in the middle of each swath. These meridians are different by exact hours from the longitude of Greenwich, England—$75°$ or 5^h (Eastern standard time), $90°$ or 6^h (Central standard time), $105°$ or 7^h (Mountain standard time), and $120°$ or 8^h (Pacific standard time). These zones take care of most of the populous areas of forty-eight of the United States and Canada; there are other zones for Alaska and Hawaii (the forty-ninth and fiftieth states) and for other areas of Canada. Note on the map of standard time zones that in well-populated areas the boundaries of the zones are irregular, to satisfy various local options. Newfoundland and Labrador have chosen a half-hour time standard, intermediate between Greenland time and Atlantic time. Texas prefers as a whole state to use Central standard time although the extreme western portion has a sundial time sixty-seven minutes earlier than that of the Central standard time meridian.

It is easy for anyone to set his watch or clock to a certain standard time, as announced, for example, by radio broadcasters. But what about a sundial, which cannot adjust itself to standard time but faithfully marks the position of the sun in the sky? Unless the sundial is located exactly on a standard time meridian ($75°$, $90°$, and so on), some allowance must be made for the difference between the lon-

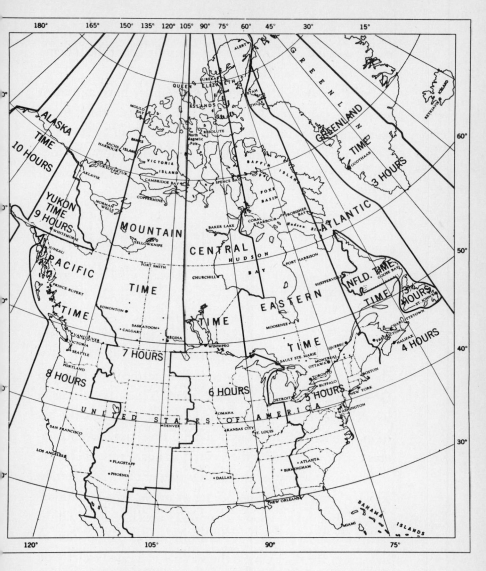

Map of standard time zones for North America and
Greenland.

gitude of the place and the longitude of the standard time meridian in use at that place.

For example, the standard time meridian for the Eastern standard time zone is $75°$, the longitude of Philadelphia. New York City, which is farther east, has a longitude close to $74°$. Therefore the sun appears to get to New York before it gets to Philadelphia. But New Yorkers have agreed to keep the same official time as that of longitude $75°$.

To use the *longitude correction,* the owner of a proper sundial must know both his longitude and that of the standard time meridian that applies to his area. If he lives east of the standard time meridian, the sun gets to him earlier than it does to the standard time meridian, so his "real" time is fast and he must *subtract* from his sundial time the time-equivalent between his place and the standard time meridian.

For example, we have seen that New York is $1°$ (or 4^m) east of Philadelphia. Now, suppose a sundial in New York indicates that the time is 12:04 P.M. A sundial in Philadelphia will not read 12:04 P.M. until the earth has turned one more degree; so in New York 4^m must be subtracted to reduce the reading to 12:00 M., in order to duplicate the reading of the proper sundial in Philadelphia at that moment. On the map, the time in minutes at each place is the longitude correction to be applied to obtain the sundial time at the Eastern standard time meridian, shown as a heavy line passing near Philadelphia. The Central

A monumental sundial erected at the New York World's Fair, 1939–1940. Designed and executed by the eminent contemporary sculptor, Paul Manship, this beautiful instrument had a gnomon about seventy feet long. It was ornamented by figures of the Fates.

standard time meridian is the broken line passing from Wisconsin through Mississippi.

If a sundial is to be erected and used at one certain place (and, of course, most of them are, as in public parks), the

A monumental sundial by Paul Manship erected at Andover, Massachusetts. This dial is of the ARMIL-LARY *type; the word armillary means formed of rings. The gnomon in the center represents the axis of the celestial sphere and casts its shadow on the time scale on the inside of the band, which represents the celestial equator.*

longitude correction can be built into the dial. The marks on the dial can be those for the appropriate standard time meridian, instead of those for the local sundial time. But while this would be possible in an expensive, monumental type of sundial, it is not feasible for a stock sundial manufactured for general sale.

As we shall see, the longitude correction and another conversion factor still to be discussed can be combined for a sundial that will not be moved more than a mile or two from the place for which it is intended. In this way only one simple bit of arithmetic need be done to convert the sundial time to the correct standard time.

• CHAPTER EIGHT •

The Equation of Time

In this chapter we shall discuss the conversion quantity that causes the most trouble to the casual reader of sundial time; sometimes sundial time is ahead of his watch time, sometimes it is slower, and confusion naturally follows. But if, as was suggested in the Preface, the sundial has the conversion quantity engraved upon it, the person who wants to know the time will see the reason for the discrepancy, and he will be able to determine the correct watch time from the sundial reading.

The local sundial time mentioned in the preceding chapter is called *local apparent solar time.* It is the time as indicated by the sun in the sky for a particular meridian of longitude. The kind of time our watches keep is *mean solar time,* based on the behavior of a convenient but purely *fictitious sun* that on the average (the mean) be-

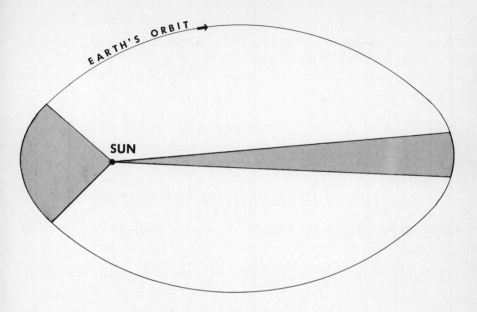

*The earth's revolution around the sun. The ellipticity
of its orbit has been greatly exaggerated.*

haves like the real sun in the sky. Mean solar time is further modified by standard time.

Nature does not always fall into man's schemes. The
early calendar makers found this true when they tried to
divide the year of the seasons into an exact number of days
to form months. The cycle of the moon's phases was
thought to be a convenient interval of time, but the value
of this month is about 29½ days; 12 such months make
up only 354 days, shorter than the seasonal year by 11
days. But the year is not an exact number of days; it is

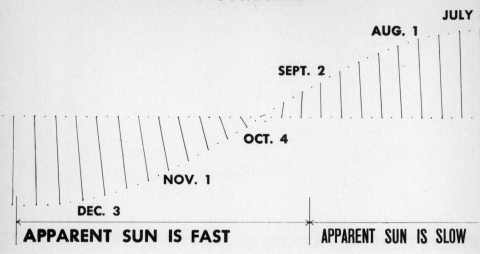

JULY

AUG. 1

SEPT. 2

OCT. 4

NOV. 1

DEC. 3

APPARENT SUN IS FAST | APPARENT SUN IS SLOW

about 365¼ days long, so 1 year in 4 has been given 366 days while the other 3 years of the group have only 365 days. The week, based upon the 7 moving bodies (the sun, the moon, and the 5 planets visible to the naked eye) the Babylonians saw in the sky, is a convenient unit of time, but it does not divide exactly into either the month or the year of the seasons.

Another problem arises when we consider using the sun as our timekeeper. As the earth turns once on its axis, it is also moving a short distance in its *orbit,* or path around the sun; so the sun appears to stand in a slightly different direction. Therefore, the earth must turn a little more than exactly once around with respect to the rest of the universe, in order to appear to have turned just once on its axis with respect to the sun.

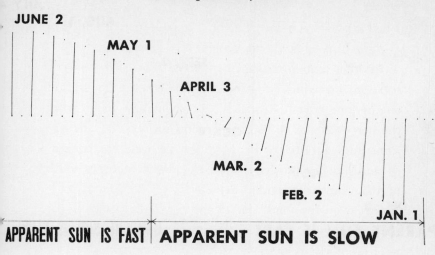

APPARENT SUN IS FAST | APPARENT SUN IS SLOW

JUNE 2

MAY 1

APRIL 3

MAR. 2

FEB. 2

JAN. 1

The race between the mean sun and the apparent sun.

If the earth's motion around the sun were very different from what it is, there would be no need to invent a mean sun; but the earth's orbit is an *ellipse,* not a circle. In the figure, the ellipticity of the earth's orbit has been greatly exaggerated. The great German astronomer Johann Kepler (1571–1630) discovered that, as the earth revolves around the sun in the course of one year, the line joining the earth and the sun sweeps over equal areas in equal times. This means that the shaded "pie-shaped" section at *perihelion,* when the earth is nearest the sun, must be wider than the shaded section at *aphelion,* when the sun and earth are farthest apart. Therefore, the earth must travel farther, in a given interval of time, at perihelion—early January, when it moves at a daily rate of $1°.019$—than at aphelion —early July, when the movement is $0°.953$.

Another motion must be considered. The earth's axis of rotation, on which it spins completely once in around twenty-four hours, is tilted by approximately $23°.5$ from the perpendicular to its orbit around the sun. So, the sun sometimes appears to be north of the celestial equator (from March 21 to September 23) and sometimes south of the celestial equator (September 23 to March 21). To get from the south side of the celestial equator to the north side, the sun's apparent path must tilt northward; to get from north to south, its path must tilt southward.

So the apparent motion of the sun eastward along its path around the earth in the course of a year is partially wasted, or at least used up, by a northward or southward motion. For this reason the sun's apparent motion eastward around the earth, while the earth is actually traveling eastward around the sun, is again uneven.

The mean sun goes eastward among the stars at a uniform rate, completing an entire revolution in one year. The mean sun, then, will sometimes be ahead of the real sun and sometimes behind it; the difference between the mean sun and the apparent sun is what is called the *equation of time.*

Astronomers know exactly how the earth moves around the sun, so the value of the equation of time can be calculated for every moment of the year. It is this value that should be engraved on every sundial that is manufactured.

It is identical on the same day for every sundial in the world, and does not depend upon location. The equation of time is only a few seconds different from one year to the next, but it returns to the same value after each leap year.

If the equation of time is applied as a conversion to the time as shown by a sundial, apparent solar time is converted to local mean solar time. Then, when the longitude correction is applied, local mean solar time is converted to standard time. With these two conversion values, standard time can be determined from a sundial, and it will agree with the time shown on our watches.

The table of values given here contains the equation of time that can be used on all sundials for any year. The plus sign (+) means that the value is to be added to the sundial time, the minus sign (−) that it should be subtracted. This does not include the longitude correction, which is different for every location; we shall consider combining the two corrections later.

Table 3. The Equation of Time

DATE	VALUE	DATE	VALUE
Jan. 1	$+ 3^m.5$	Feb. 16	+ 14.2
6	+ 5.8	21	+ 13.7
11	+ 7.9	26	+ 13.0
16	+ 9.8	Mar. 1	+ 12.5
21	+ 11.3	6	+ 11.4
26	+ 12.6	11	+ 10.2
Feb. 1	+ 13.4	16	+ 8.8
6	+ 14.1	21	+ 7.4
11	+ 14.3	26	+ 5.8

An early eighteenth-century brass sundial from Germany. The instrument has a provision for applying the equation of time in the small mechanism in the foreground. Leveling screws and a small plumb-bob (at the middle of the base of the gnomon) permit setting of the sundial.

DATE		VALUE		DATE		VALUE	
Apr.	1	+	4.0	Aug.	16	+	4.3
	6	+	2.6		21	+	3.2
	11	+	1.2		26	+	1.9
	16	−	0.1	Sep.	1	+	0.1
	21	−	1.2		6	−	1.5
	26	−	2.1		11	−	3.2
May	1	−	2.9		16	−	5.0
	6	−	3.4		21	−	6.8
	11	−	3.6		26	−	8.5
	16	−	3.7	Oct.	1	−	10.2
	21	−	3.5		6	−	11.7
	26	−	3.1		11	−	13.1
June	1	−	2.3		16	−	14.3
	6	−	1.5		21	−	15.2
	11	−	0.6		26	−	15.9
	16	+	0.4	Nov.	1	−	16.4
	21	+	1.6		6	−	16.3
	26	+	2.6		11	−	16.0
July	1	+	$3^m.9$		16	−	15.2
	6	+	4.6		21	−	14.2
	11	+	5.3		26	−	12.8
	16	+	5.9	Dec.	1	−	11.0
	21	+	6.2		6	−	9.0
	26	+	6.4		11	−	6.9
Aug.	1	+	6.3		16	−	4.5
	6	+	5.8		21	−	2.0
	11	+	5.2		26	+	0.4

It will be seen that the above table gives the value of the equation of time for each five days, and to within six seconds. No one can consult a sundial in the hope of obtaining the time accurately to the nearest few seconds. In fact, no one should trust his watch to only a few seconds,

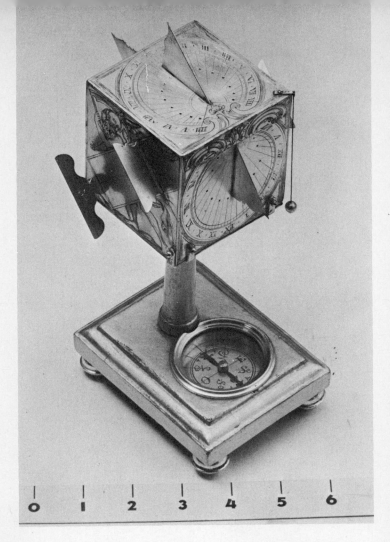

A many-sided early eighteenth-century sundial of
wood and silver, made in Vienna. The plumb-bob,
leveling screws, and magnetic compass were used to
set it. Because the gnomons are not all parallel with
each other, various faces of the dial may have been
intended to tell the time for different places.

A many-faced sundial from about 1700.

unless he has just heard a radio time signal. These signals
are inserted by some networks and individual radio and
television stations as a "beep," or as a soft bell tone, and
they are quite accurate, because the government demands

that such a definite signal be correct to a fraction of a second. Before this standardization, when a radio announcer would say that at the next sound of the gong it would be such-and-such a time, he had the button right in his booth. Since he could push it at any time he wished, he was usually incorrect by many seconds.

The sundial that can be constructed from the cutout included in this book lists the equation of time for each ten days and to the nearest minute. These values will be sufficient to determine the correct standard time to within a minute or two, which is close enough for most practical purposes.

Another factor adds to the confusion of those who do not understand sundials—daylight saving time, which is one hour later than standard time. This is a purely arbitrary device, designed to give urban dwellers an extra hour of daylight in the evening, after their workday. Farmers, as a rule, do not like daylight saving time, so in rural areas standard time is often used used throughout the year. Some cities use daylight saving time from the last Sunday in April to the last Sunday in September, while others continue it until the last Sunday in October.

When sundial time is converted to standard time, an additional hour may have to be added if daylight saving time is used in that particular area.

CHAPTER NINE

The Complete Correction
to a Sundial

It is something of a paradox to use the term "correction" of a sundial. How can we correct something that is true? As explained earlier, a correctly made and correctly set sundial tells accurately the kind of time for which it is intended. It is because of the special needs of our modern civilization that the sundial is not the kind of timer that we need for our sophisticated lives. A sundial is the perfect timekeeper; no known mechanical device—watch, clock, crystal clock—can accurately tell the way the earth is really rotating; the sundial can. Although the sundial is an interesting and historically important instrument, from the practical point of view a watch costing only a few dollars

*A monumental sundial in the garden of the Morehead
Planetarium of the University of North Carolina at
Chapel Hill. (The sundial is a gift of the New York
industrialist and philanthropist John Motley Morehead.) The gnomon is about twenty feet long.*

can serve us better today. A little piece of machinery on our wall or on our wrist is, in a way, an expression of man's ingenuity in our time. But thirty-five centuries ago, when civilization was fairly young, the sundial was also a triumph of man's intelligence.

Two conversion factors that must be applied to sundial time to obtain correct watch time have been discussed. One of them depends upon the longitude of the place where the sundial is set up; the other, depending upon the shape of the earth's orbit around the sun, is the equation of time. And in this chapter, we shall determine how to combine the two, for any particular sundial, to obtain standard time.

It should first be recalled that the longitude correction is a *constant* for any particular place where the sundial is set up, while the equation of time changes for each day of the year no matter where the sundial may be located. A tabulation of corrections to the sundial for each day of the year, or five days, or ten days is still necessary. But we can combine the two "corrections" so that only one addition to or subtraction from the sundial time will yield the standard time.

Perhaps the best way to approach this is to use an example. The longitude of the Adler Planetarium, on a peninsula in Lake Michigan, is $87°36'24''$ west of Greenwich. Chicago uses Central standard time, and the meridian for that is $90°$ west of Greenwich. The difference between these two values is $2°23'36''$.

The Adler Planetarium and Astronomical Museum, operated by the Chicago Park District.

This angular longitude difference is equal to $9^m34^s.4$, which can be rounded off to $9^m.6$ (we shall be only $1^s.6$ wrong, if we do). This is the difference between the Adler Planetarium and the Central standard time meridian.

Because the Adler Planetarium is east of the standard time meridian (its longitude is less than $90°$), the sundial time at Adler is always fast, and $9^m.6$ must always be subtracted from the sundial to obtain the time that, at the same moment, would be shown on a sundial located at the Central time meridian.

The Complete Correction to a Sundial

Now we go back to the equation of time, given for each five days of the year on p. 79. To obtain the *complete* correction to a sundial set up correctly at the Adler Planetarium, each of the values of the equation of time is combined with the $-9^m.6$ longitude correction. For example, the equation of time for January 1 is $+3^m.5$; combined with the longitude correction, the final value is $-6^m.1$.

The new table would start out like this:

*Table 4.   Sample Table of Corrections to Obtain
Standard Time*

DATE	CORR.
Jan. 1	$- 6^m.1$
6	$- 3.8$
11	$- 1.7$
16	$+ 0.2$
21	$+ 1.7$
26	$+ 3.0$

Such a final table of corrections from the sundial reading to the correct standard time could be attached to the base of a monumental sundial correctly designed and set up at any place; all that is required is to combine the equation of time and the correct longitude time difference between the location and the standard time meridian. Then, to determine the correct time, only one easy addition or subtraction instead of two need be performed.

But it was suggested earlier that a sundial manufactured for general sale cannot include such a complete correction table, because it is likely that every one sold will be set up in a different longitude. In that case, the equation of time table should always be included. The purchaser must determine his own longitude correction, or have it done for him. Then the two corrections must be made separately, when reading the sundial, unless the dial can be altered to include the longitude automatically. This process will be described in the next chapter.

CHAPTER TEN

A Cutout Sundial

Now that the underlying principles of sundials have been discussed, it will be possible to follow the instructions below in order to make a sundial that can be correctly set up and will operate properly in any latitude or longitude in either hemisphere. The direction and most of the lettering are intended for the northern hemisphere, but the alterations necessary for the southern hemisphere will be given at the end of this chapter. The adjustment for latitude is very simple. The time dial, as will be explained below, can be offset to include the longitude correction automatically, so only the equation of time need be applied, day by day, to convert from sundial time to standard time.

While it is suggested that poster board or illustration board (cardboard of high quality) be used, an ambitious hobbyist who likes to work with plastics can use sheets of

The completed equatorial sundial.

this material for greater rigidity and durability. In any event, it might be useful to spray the final product with a transparent lacquer to seal it against humidity. Because this cutout example is intended more as an educational device than as a garden ornament, it should be set up in such a way that it can be removed during times of inclement weather, then replaced accurately. Two removable screws through the base near the words "East" and "West" can attach the instrument to its base and allow the sundial to be moved.

The directions given below are as explicit as possible. The parts of the entire model are shown on sheets A, B, and C (pp. 99–103; another set is printed on pp. 105–109). Each sheet has been printed twice so that two equatorial sundials can be constructed.

1. Sheet A shows the two faces of the time dial. Note that on one the numerals run clockwise, on the other counterclockwise, so that when they are assembled, back to back, the corresponding numbers on the two sides will coincide. Cement the whole sheet flat on illustration board (cardboard) at least 1/16th inch thick. When quite dry, cut out the two arcs carefully with an Exacto knife or a razor blade in a holder, making sure that the cut is perpendicular to the face of the sheet. Then cement the two arcs back to back, so the lines of the two faces match exactly. Dry the assembly under a weight such as a heavy book, so it will come out quite flat and unwarped.

2. Cement sheet B, containing the elements of the supporting cradle, flat on a sheet of illustration board and dry thoroughly before the various parts are cut out. Separate the east and west faces of the cradle at the horizontal line above the abbreviation LAT (for latitude), and separate the piece marked buttresses into two identical pieces along the vertical line. These two will later be cemented perpendicular to the east and west faces of the cradle, along the dotted lines, and perpendicular also to the base (on Sheet C), along the dotted lines. The buttresses serve to support the cradle in a vertical position.

3. The cradle is a sandwich, with the middle layer cemented between the east and west faces with the long straight edges and the lazy reversed curves of the vertical edges coinciding exactly. This leaves a groove all along the circular edge; later the meridian arc will lie in this groove. Again, as with the time dial, this assembly must be dried under a heavy weight to insure that it will come out quite flat. Before the cement has completely set, run the tip of a nail file or a scissors blade along the groove to remove any of the cement that may have oozed out to obstruct the groove.

4. Cement Sheet C to illustration board, of the same thickness as that used for Sheet B, because the semicircular meridian arc must fit neatly into the groove of the cradle, in the final assembly. Again, cut out this meridian arc and the square which forms the base when the cement is quite dry. The base can be further strengthened by cementing it

to a much heavier piece of illustration board or perhaps a piece of masonite, cut out so it extends about ¼ inch on all sides beyond the base. The corner of the base with the cross-line dotted across the diagonal will be the north.

5. Now cement the supporting cradle vertically along the indicated diagonal of the base, with the high portion to the north. To maintain the vertical position of the cradle, cement the two buttresses along the dotted cross-line of the base and the dotted line.on each face of the cradle.

6. Now cement the meridian arc of Sheet C and the assembled double-thickness time dial of Sheet A at right angles to each other at their centers. The heavy black area in the inside middle of the meridian arc indicates a notch that must be accurately cut out, exactly as wide as the double-thickness time dial is thick. At first it might be cut deliberately a trifle too narrow, then widened by a sliver or two on each side until the time dial fits tightly into it.

7. A notch must be cut into the outside of the middle of the time dial around the noon mark, but here a decision must be made. If the finished sundial is to be considered truly universal, adaptable to any latitude and longitude, the notch in the time dial must be cut so that it is exactly centered on the 12 noon mark. Then, to determine standard time, both the longitude correction and the equation of time must be applied to the sundial reading.

If the sundial is to be used in a fixed location, the longitude correction can be built into it by cutting the notch in the time dial to one side or the other of the exact 12 mark.

Then, to determine the standard time, only the equation of time need be added to the sundial reading. To do this, the longitude correction is determined according to the instructions in Chapter 7. This will be the time-distance to one side or the other of the 12 noon mark that will be the center of the notch. If the place is east of the standard time meridian, cut the notch with its center at a point earlier than noon by the amount of the longitude correction. If the place is west of the standard time meridian, cut the notch at a point later than the noon mark by the amount of the longitude correction. When this decision has been made, the notch can be cut, carefully.

8. First mark out the center line for it at the proper place on the dial. We have already provided for the notch in the meridian arc to be just as wide as the thickness of the time dial, and of the depth shown on Sheet C. The width of the notch in the outside rim of the time dial should be a trifle more than the thickness of the supporting cradle, which is three thicknesses of illustration board. Its depth should be such that the inside edges of the dial and the meridian arc are exactly flush with each other.

For a sundial in the northern hemisphere, the north face of the time dial, with the numbers reading clockwise, should face toward the end of the meridian arc that has the numbered latitude graduations on it. Then the two must be cemented firmly together exactly at right angles to each other. When the cement has partially set, this correct alignment can be checked by laying one ruler on edge between the two ends of the meridian arc and measuring the distance from this ruler to the 6 A.M. and 6 P.M. marks on the time dial. Then, the ruler can be laid with its edge across the two 6 o'clock lines and the distance from its center point measured to various parts of the meridian arc. These must all be equal. The assembly can be "teased" a little, one way or another, while the cement is setting, to make sure that these conditions are fulfilled.

9. Now we are ready to set the time assembly into the slot or groove of the supporting cradle. The graduated end of the meridian arc is the higher end and the appropriate value of the latitude on the meridian arc must be set at the top of the supporting cradle, marked LAT. If the dial is to be used at a fixed location, cement the arc in this position. But if the universal character of the instrument is to be demonstrated, leave the meridian arc free to be moved higher or lower in the cradle; the slot is long enough and must be tight enough to hold the arc in place, or a small drop of cement might tack it into the correct latitude position for semipermanent use.

10. But as yet we have no gnomon! Therefore, cement a thin wire, like a very straight piece of wire clothes hanger, or something thinner, to the ends of the meridian arc, spanning the gap between them. The center line of the wire must coincide with the ends of the meridian arc; if it is too thick, shave a little material from each end of the arc. When the gnomon has been cemented into position, make a final checkup by measuring to see if all parts of the time

dial and the meridian arc are equally distant from the gnomon. A little warping this way or that, and a slight addition of cement, will preserve the final correct alignment.

The table for the conversion of the sundial reading to standard time will depend on the decision made earlier when placing the notch in the time dial, as has been explained. The table can be typed and arranged in such form as to be cut apart and cemented to the base of the sundial, on either side of the supporting cradle, with the instruction: TO OBTAIN STANDARD TIME, APPLY THE CORRECTION BELOW.

11. Only one thing remains to be done: to mount the sundial properly. If it is to be set on a post, the top of the post must be exactly horizontal, as checked with a carpenter's level. Then the base of the sundial must be attached to the post in such a way as to have the meridian arc exactly in the north-south line. Sighting along a magnetic compass needle is no good for this, because magnetic north and true north agree with each other only in a few places in the world. It is better to make the sundial set itself.

From a radio time signal, set your watch exactly. Next, look up the equation of time for the date and use this and the longitude correction to determine just what time the sundial should indicate when the watch reads some certain time. For example, suppose the date is October 21. The equation of time for that day is -15^m. Assume that the longitude correction is -10^m. The sum of the two is -25^m. This means that 25 minutes must be subtracted from the sundial at that place and on that date to obtain the correct standard time. But it must mean also that, if you have the correct standard time, 25 minutes must be added to it, to obtain correct sundial time. So, by adding 25 minutes to the time indicated by the watch, the time that the sundial should indicate can be determined, and the instrument can be rotated on the top of the post until that time is indicated.

The attachment screws to hold the sundial on the post can be put through holes drilled through two opposite corners of the square base; if they are made to fit a bit loosely, the final adjustment is somewhat easier before the screws are driven home. As has been suggested earlier, it would be advisable to be able to withdraw the screws so the sundial can be taken inside the house for protection against the weather. At almost any hardware or variety store, aerosol cans of clear lacquer or varnish can be purchased. Spraying the instrument with this material on a good, dry, sunny day will seal it and help to keep out moisture for a long time; it will produce very little, if any, discoloration of the printed surfaces.

CHANGES NECESSARY FOR THE
SOUTHERN HEMISPHERE

The high end of the meridian arc is now to the south. But in cementing the time dial and the meridian arc together, the side of the dial turned toward the latitude markings should be the one on which the time markings increase counterclockwise. Of course, the east and west faces of the supporting cradle have now been reversed, but this does not affect the operation of the sundial. No other change is necessary.

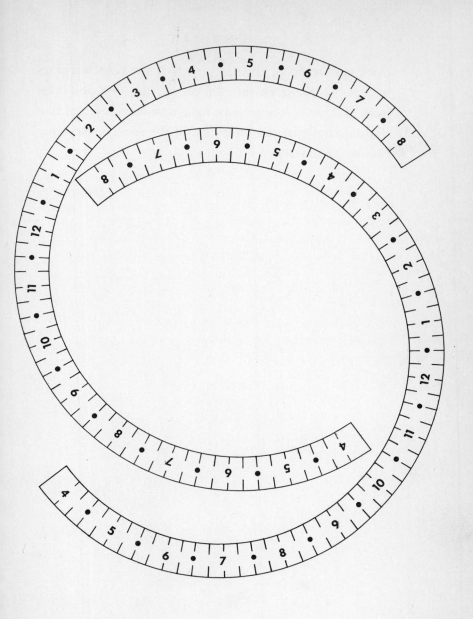

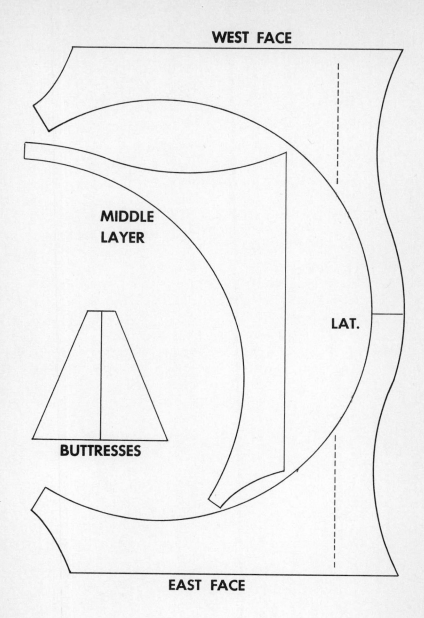

WEST FACE

MIDDLE
LAYER

BUTTRESSES

LAT.

EAST FACE

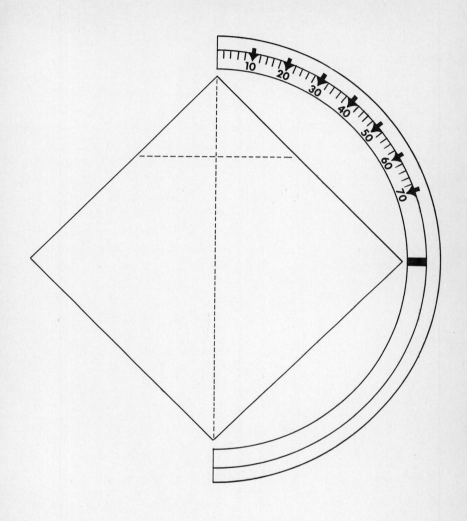

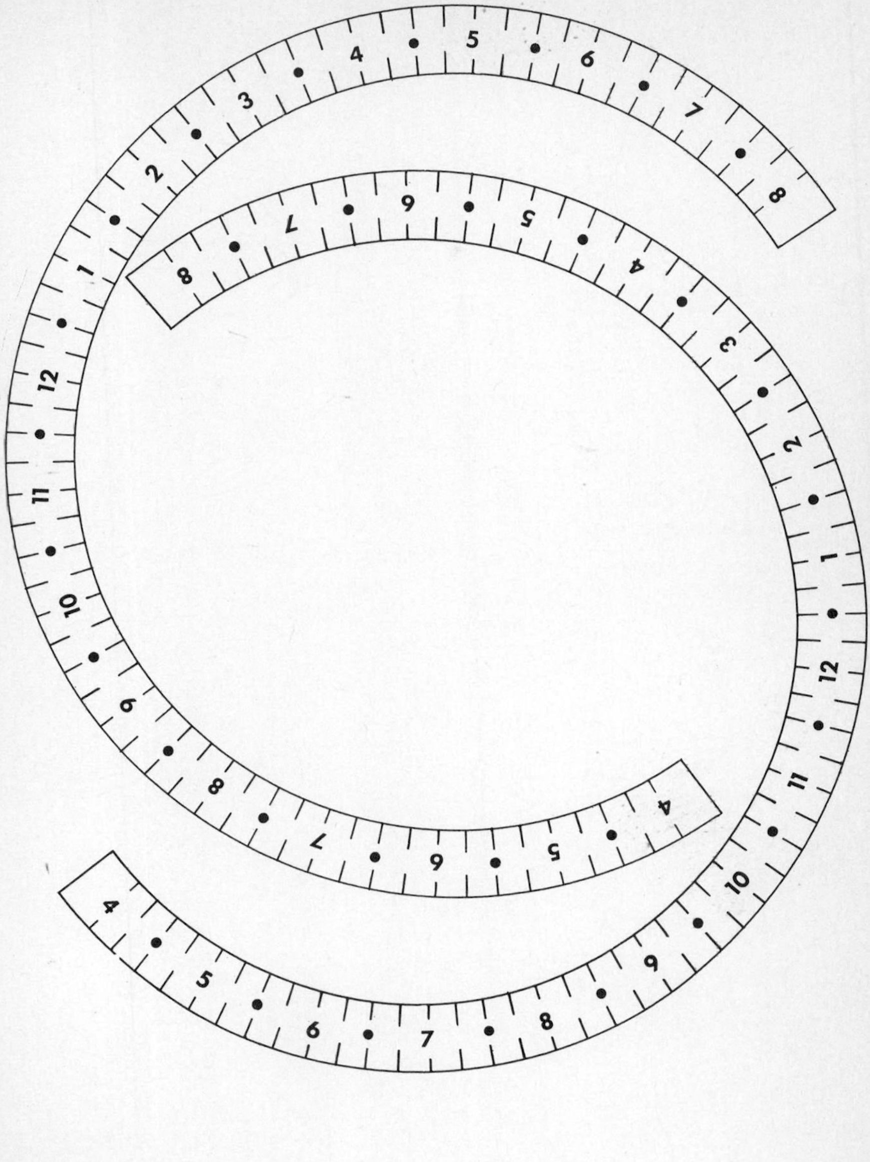

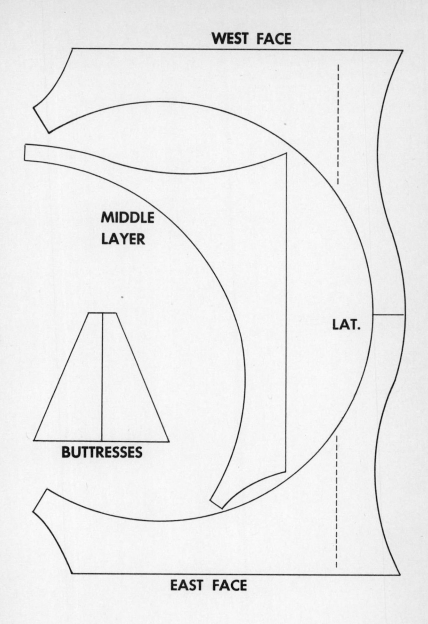

WEST FACE

MIDDLE
LAYER

LAT.

BUTTRESSES

EAST FACE

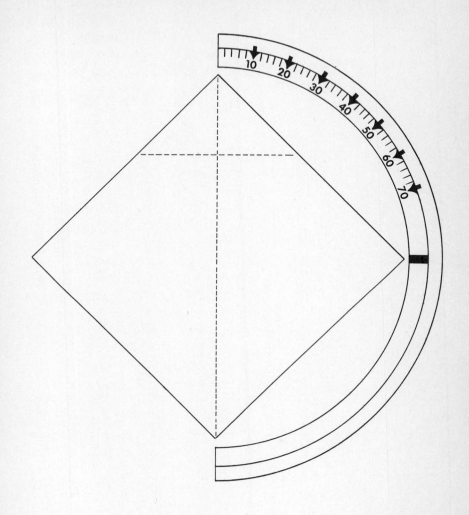

Glossary

altitude   The distance of an object measured vertically from the horizon and expressed in degrees, minutes, and seconds of arc.

angular measurement   The measure of the portion of a circle included between two lines drawn from the center of the circle. The whole circumference of a circle is divided into 360 equal parts called degrees; if the two lines from the center mark off an eighth of the circumference, for example, the angle is 45 degrees. Degrees are subdivided into 60 minutes; each minute is divided into 60 seconds. See *arc*.

ante meridiem (A.M.)   The part of the day from midnight to noon.

aphelion   The point in the earth's orbit (or that of any planet) at which the planet is at its greatest distance from the sun and moves most slowly along the orbit.

apparent daily motion   The motion of the sun or other object caused by the motion of the earth. As the earth rotates on its axis from west to east (counterclockwise as viewed from the North Pole), objects in the sky have apparent motion from east to west. As the earth revolves annually around the sun, the sun appears to revolve around the earth. See *revolution* and *rotation.*

apparent solar time   The time as indicated by the apparent sun (the sun we see in the sky), as marked by the length of time before it will cross the celestial meridian of the place, or the length of time since it crossed the meridian.

arc   A portion of the circumference of a circle, expressed in degrees, minutes, and seconds of angular measurement.

astrolabe   Invented or at least improved by Hipparchus, about 130 B.C., this instrument was used, even in medieval Europe and into early modern times, to determine position on land or sea and for solving other problems in navigation and time determination.

celestial equator   The imaginary great circle exactly over the earth's equator, dividing the heavens into northern and southern hemispheres. See *rotation.*

celestial meridian   See *meridian.*

celestial poles   The points in the heavens exactly over the earth's North and South Poles.

clepsydra   Any one of several forms of water clock whose operation depended on the slow flow of water, either to empty or to fill a container. The name comes from the Greek *klepto* (to steal) and *hydro* (water).

day   Correctly, the period of rotation of the earth on its axis. If taken with respect to the sun (for example, from noon to the next succeeding noon), it is the solar day; if taken with respect to some certain star, it is the *sidereal* day (for example, from one rising of the star to the next succeeding rising of the same star).

degree   The angle between two lines drawn from the center of a circle, if the arc or portion of the circumference of the circle between the two lines is exactly 1/360 of the whole.

dialling   The art of designing and using sundials and other instruments, such as astrolabes.

ellipse   A curved figure of any shape, varying from a circle to a straight line, that can be seen if a circular disk (such as a phonograph record) is viewed at various angles, or is tilted by various amounts.

ecliptic   The earth's orbit or annual path around the sun, as projected on the celestial sphere.

equation of time   The amount of time by which the apparent sun that we see in the sky is ahead of or behind the mean sun. Its value is zero on four dates of the year (about April 15, June 15, September 1, and December 25). On February 12, the mean sun is more than 14 minutes ahead of the apparent sun; on May 15, the mean sun is almost 4 minutes behind; on July 26, the mean sun is about 6½ minutes ahead;

on November 3, the mean sun is almost 16½ minutes behind.

equator   The imaginary circle around the earth, dividing the earth's surface into northern and southern hemispheres. It lies midway between the North and South Poles of the earth. There is also a celestial equator, defined above.

fictitious sun   See *mean sun.*

gnomon   The style, or shadow-casting portion of a sundial.

Greenwich   The suburb of London, England, through which passes the meridian that has been chosen as the zero meridian, and from which longitude is measured east or west to the meridian passing through some other place.

hemicyclium   An ancient form of sundial in which (usually) a horizontal gnomon cast its shadow on marks engraved on the inside of a portion of a sphere.

hemispherium   An ancient form of sundial in which a gnomon, either horizontal, vertical or slanted, cast its shadow on the inside surface of a spherical bowl.

horizon   The line around an observer where the sky seems to meet the water (at sea), or the land (on a flat terrestrial area).

hour   The 24th part of the rotation period of the earth, referred to the mean sun.

hourglass   See *sand glass.*

latitude   The angular distance of a place from the earth's equator, measured along the meridian passing through the place. North of the equator, latitudes are north (N.) or plus (+) ; south of the equator, latitudes are south (S.) or minus (−).

longitude   The angular distance, measured along the equator, from the point where the meridian of Greenwich crosses the equator to the point where the meridian of another place crosses the equator. Longitudes are measured for 12 hours, or 180 degrees, both eastward and westward from the Greenwich meridian. See *Greenwich.*

longitude correction   That permanent correction factor to a sundial that is not located exactly on a standard time meridian.

mean solar time   The time as marked by the mean sun, or the amount of time before the mean sun will cross the meridian over a place, or the amount of time since the mean sun has crossed the meridian.

mean sun   Invented to smooth out the irregular or non-uniform motion of the apparent sun. The mean sun is assumed to travel apparently eastward along the celestial equator at a uniform rate, while the apparent sun is seen to travel at a nonuniform rate in a general easterly direction along the ecliptic.

meridian   An imaginary circle on the earth or (celestial meridian) on the sky, passing exactly through the North and South Poles of the earth or sky and crossing the equator at right angles. The celestial meridian for a place cuts the sky into eastern and western halves passing, as it does, exactly through the zenith and the north and south points of the horizon. See *Greenwich*.

meridiem Literally, middle of the day. This is the moment of noon, abbreviated as M. or 12:00 M.

minute The sixtieth part of an hour of time or the sixtieth part of a degree of arc. The context usually makes clear which is meant.

noon The moment when the sun has traversed half of its path across the sky during the day. Mean noon refers to the mean or fictitious sun; apparent noon (high noon, sundial noon) is a reference to the apparent sun which we see in the sky.

perihelion The point in the earth's orbit (or that of any planet) at which the planet is at its least distance from the sun and moves most rapidly in its orbit.

post meridiem (P.M.) That portion of the day from noon to midnight.

revolution The motion of one body around another, or around some point outside the body. The earth revolves around the sun.

rotation The motion of a body around an axis within itself. The earth rotates on its axis, producing the succession of nights and days.

sand glass Sometimes called hour glass, but many sand glasses mark intervals of time longer or shorter than one hour. The flow of sand from one portion of the glass container to the other (provided the sand remains dry) marks the flow of time.

second   The sixtieth part of a minute of time or the sixtieth part a minute of arc. The context usually makes clear which is meant.

standard time   The mean solar time for an arbitrarily chosen meridian of longitude, which time by agreement will be considered that for use over a wide strip north and south on the earth's surface.

style   The gnomon or shadow-casting edge of a sundial.

water clock   See *clepsydra*.

zenith   The point in the heavens exactly over the observer or place.

Suggestions for Further Reading

BENSON, JAMES W., *Time and Time-tellers,* London, Robert Banks & Son, 1902.
This old book has a good historical section, greatly detailed but sometimes inaccurate.

BREARLEY, HARRY C., *Time Telling through the Ages,* New York, Doubleday, 1919.
Written for a watch company, this book has an excellent dictionary of terms and many illustrations in an appendix.

COWAN, HARRISON J., *Time and Its Measurement,* Cleveland and New York, The World Publishing Co., 1958.
Much interesting material, from the simple gnomon to the most modern clocks and watches. Instructions for the construction of a horizontal sundial are given.

EARLE, ALICE MORSE, *Sundials and Roses of Yesterday,*
New York, The Macmillan Company, 1922.
Many illustrations showing interesting sundials, inscriptions,
and rose gardens.

GATTY, H. K. F. AND LLOYD, ELEANOR, *The Book of
Sundials,* London, George Bell and Sons, 1900.
Hundreds of sketches and inscriptions on dials.

MAYALL, R. NEWTON AND MAYALL, MARGARET WAL-
TON, *Sundials,* Boston, Hale, 1938.
This book, written by an architect and his astronomer wife,
contains many illustrations and instructions for making
many kinds of sundials.

Under the headings of SUNDIALS and TIME, library card
catalogues and encyclopedias may be consulted for further
reading materials.

Acknowledgments

The author would like to acknowledge the following sources for illustrations in the volume: Frontispiece, courtesy of The American Museum of Natural History; The Bettman Archive, p. 34; The Chicago Park District, p. 86; The Mensing Collection, pp. 32, 33, 36, 49, 50, 57, 78, 80, 81; The New York Public Library, p. 35; Paul Manship, pp. 69, 70; and the University of North Carolina Photo Lab, p. 84.

Index

Index

About the Author

DR. ROY K. MARSHALL is a distinguished popularizer of astronomy. He is a former research astronomer at Yerkes Observatory and Harvard Observatory; former Director of Fels and Morehead Planetariums; former Professor of Astronomy at the University of North Carolina; and former Science Editor of the *Philadelphia Evening Bulletin*. He has written a number of books, including *The Nature of Things* and *Sun, Moon and Planets*.

About the Illustrator

JERRY CAILOR, a young New York artist beginning his professional career, is a graduate of Syracuse University where he majored in advertising illustrating. He is presently employed by Horn/Griner, a photographic design studio that does independent work for many advertising agencies. Born in Youngstown, Ohio, Mr. Cailor now lives with his wife in Flushing, New York.